Production of Prodigiosin – Like Pigment From Serratia Marcescens

Neethu Asokan
Jiji K. M.
Hemalatha N.

Production of Prodigiosin – Like Pigment From Serratia Marcescens

Optimized Media and Oil Refinery Effluent Formulated Media

LAP LAMBERT Academic Publishing

Imprint
Any brand names and product names mentioned in this book are subject to trademark, brand or patent protection and are trademarks or registered trademarks of their respective holders. The use of brand names, product names, common names, trade names, product descriptions etc. even without a particular marking in this work is in no way to be construed to mean that such names may be regarded as unrestricted in respect of trademark and brand protection legislation and could thus be used by anyone.

Cover image: www.ingimage.com

Publisher:
LAP LAMBERT Academic Publishing
is a trademark of
International Book Market Service Ltd., member of OmniScriptum Publishing Group
17 Meldrum Street, Beau Bassin 71504, Mauritius

Printed at: see last page
ISBN: 978-620-0-47823-8

Contents

Screening of new strain *Serratia* which produced prodigiosin and to optimize the culture medium for effective pigment production. The aim of study is to identify optimized medium composition to achieve more efficient production of a prodigiosin-like pigment (PLP) from *Serratia marcescence*. Prodigiosin should be produced in large quantities to be able to meet future needs.

1. Characteristic of Prodigiosin:

Prodigiosin was a characteristic member of a group of compounds with a common pyrrolylpyrromethene (PPM) skeleton and had a series of close relatives bearing the same PPM core with different alkyl substituents (Pandey *et al.*, 2003, Furstner *et al.*, 2003). Prodigiosin had been shown to be associated in extracellular vesicles, cell associated or present in intracellular granules. When discussing the eco physiological role of prodigiosins, we had to take into account that a considerable part of the genetic material of the producing strains and more than 20 genes or 30 kbp was dedicated to their synthesis, underpinning the importance of these molecules.

The production of prodigiosin in *S. marcescens* was susceptible to temperature and is substantially inhibited at temperatures higher than 37°C (Furstner *et al.*, 2004 and Yamashita *et al.*, 2001). Conventional media used for the biosynthesis of prodigiosin by *S. marcescens* strains are complex media that are rich in a variety of nutrients (Furstner, A 2003, Giri, A.V., Anandkumar *et al.*, 2004, Yamashita *et al.*, 2001). Certain nutrients, such as thiamine (Goldschmitt *et al.*, 1968) and ferric acid (Silverman *et al.*, 1973), are particularly crucial for prodigiosin production, whereas phosphate (Witney *et al.*, 1977), adenosine triphosphate, and ribose (Lawanson *et al.*, 1975) have inhibitory effects on prodigiosin yield (Yu-Hong We *et al.*, 2005).

Luria Bertani (LB) broth was shown to be an effective growth medium for *Serratia marcescence*. LB broth was used as the basal medium for the medium improvement. The components of LB broth examined for their effects on prodigiosin production. The effect of vegetable oil effluent and used cooking also investigated for prodigiosin production.

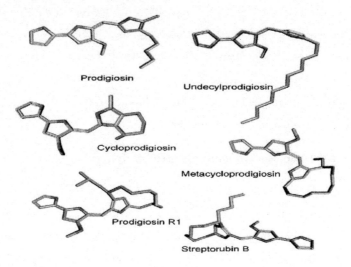

Prodigiosin

Undecylprodigiosin

Cycloprodigiosin

Metacycloprodigiosin

Prodigiosin R1

Streptorubin B

2. Benefits of Prodigiosin:

Emergence of algicidal bacteria including prodigiosin was boon for aquatic life. Prodigiosin was a natural red pigment with algicidal activity against *Cochlodinium polykrikoides*, a major harmful red tide micro alga (Kamble K.D, Hiwarale V.D., 2012).

Prodigiosin possesses immunosuppressive, antifungal and antiproliferative properties (Soto-Cerrato *et al.*, 2004 and Montaner *et al.*, 2001). It also induces apoptosis in certain cancer cells (Furstner.A 2003, Montaner *et al.*, 2001 and Watanabe *et al.*, 2000 and Montaner, B., Navarro *et al.*, 2000). Prodigiosin induced apoptosis in cancer cell lines by the characteristic DNA laddering pattern and condensed nuclei or apoptotic bodies. A synergistic inhibitory activity of prodigiosin and chitinolytic enzymes was observed against spore germination of *Botrytis cinerea.*

2. a) The anticancer activity of prodigiosin:

The anticancer effect of prodigiosin had drawn great attention recently owing to its potent cytotoxicity against a wide range of human cancer cell lines and its proapoptotic effect selectively biosurfactant against malignant cells irrespective of p53 status or multidrug resistance. Prodigiosin was subjected to preclinical trials for pancreatic cancer treatment. Prodigiosin to induce apoptosis through the mitochondrial pathway. Prodigiosins are of interest because they might have potential clinical utility.

2. b) Prodigiosin red pigments used for dye:

Dyeing of wool, cotton and silk fabrics with this rose red microbial pigment as natural dye indicated that the colour strength values and the dye uptake were high with satisfactory fastness properties of the dyed fabric (Alihosseini *et al.*2008). Prodigiosin used as a natural dye for dyeing of natural fabrics. In addition to dye ability, various features of microbial dyes like their natural character, biodegradability, production being independent of seasons and large scale production using industrially controlled fermentation technologies make it a potential candidate as an alternate to the various available chemically synthesized dyes.

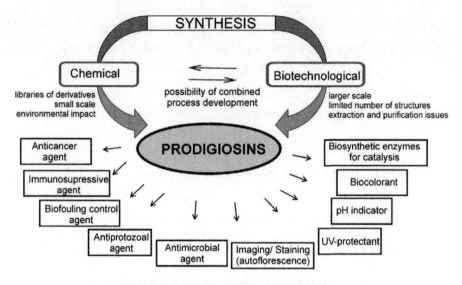

PROPERTIES & APPLICATIONS

2. c) Antimicrobial activity of Prodigiosin:

Prodigiosin had antimicrobial activity to help *S. marcescens* survive in nature (San-Lang Wang *et al.*, 2012). The pigment produced by *Vibrio* spp isolated from marine sediments to generate a large quantity of prodiginines which were used as a clothing dye. When the pigment was applied on most of the tested fabrics, strong antibacterial activity was proved (Alihosseini *et al.*, 2008). prodigiosin-producing *S.marcescens* was a stick to hydrophobic surfaces, while non-prodigiosin-producing species will not. Therefore, prodigiosin might help *S. marcescens* attach to the hydrophobic surface in its natural habitat (Rear *et al.*, 1992).

2. d) Antibacterial activity:

Antimicrobial effects of various prodigiosins were described way back in the pre-penicillin era (historical summary given in Bennett and Bentley 2000).Since the mid-1970s, antibacterial activity of purified bacterial prodigiosins has been repeatedly reported but shadowed by the more

5

pronounced and promising anticancer and immunosuppressive activities of the same molecules. Accumulated data showed an extremely broad spectrum of antimicrobial activity depends on the prodigiosin structure. Minimal inhibitory concentrations against both Gram-negative and gram positive bacteria were between 10 and 100µgml^{-1} (Nada Stankovic *et al.*, 2014).

Prodigiosins can express antibacterial effect not only as antibiotic agents but indirectly by preventing bacterial biofilm formation with high antifouling activity against marine fouling bacteria like *Alteromonas* sp., *Gallionella* sp., and cyanobacteria (Priya *et al.*, 2013).

2. e) Antifungal Activity:

Prodigiosin activity against pathogenic fungi was also described early and prodigiosin was experimentally used as a fungicidal agent against Coccidioides immitis, but venous sclerosis occurred on injection of the formulation with glutamic acid (Williams and Hearn 1967).The antifungal spectrum of prodigiosins is also broad and includes species of *Candida, Aspergillus, Penicillium, Saccharomyces, Cryptococcus,* and *Histoplasma.*   .

It was shown that purified undecylprodigiosin strongly reduced microsclerotia formation when added to the growing V. dahliae in vitro, and the presence of growing undecylprodigiosin producing strain led to an efficient reduction of *V. dahliae* hyphae and microsclerotia on *Arabidopsis thaliana* roots (Meschke et al. 2012).

The role of *S. marcescens* as producer of chitinases in biocontrol of plant fungal pathogens has been well established (Jones et al. 1986; Monreal and Reese 1969).

Novel research suggests that prodigiosins could also find application as antifungal agents combating crop disease.

2. f) Antimalarial activity:

Prodigiosins have been shown to act as antimalarials in the 1960s (Castro 1967), but this feature stayed the least studied one, until recently, when intensive research was undertaken including a comparative molecular similarity index analysis model generation to explore the structural features influencing prodigiosin antimalarial activity (Mahajan et al. 2012, 2013;Papireddy et al. 2011; Singh et al. 2013).Prodigiosin, undecylprodigiosin, and metacycloprodigiosin were shown to exhibit potent in vitro activity against *Plasmodium falciparum.*

Prodigiosin from S. marcescens NMCC46 was reported to be efficient mosquito larvicidal agent against species of *Aedes aegypti* and *Anopheles stephensi* (Patil et al. 2012) paving the path of prodigiosin application as insecticides.

2. g) Antitrypanosomal activity:

The first reports of antitrypanosomal activity of bacterial prodigiosins date back to the 1950s, when McRary and coworkers established its in vitro activity against Trypanosoma cruzi to be relatively rapid and determined the active concentration of 10 µg ml−1 (McRary et al. 1953).

Prodigiosin from S. marcescens interferes with the oxidative phosphorylation processes in the mitochondria of T. cruzi leading to parasite cell death with no toxic effects on human cells (Genes *et al.*,2011).. These findings make prodigiosin a promising drug for combating protozoan-mediated diseases such as Chagas disease that is a serious health threat with limited treatment options.

2. i) Antialgal activity:

Early findings showed that prodigiosin from *S. marcescens* had anti-algal effect on *Prototheca zopfi* (Gerber1975). Similarly to antibacterial activity, prodigiosin exhibits a broad antialgal spectrum. It was proposed that marine bacteria producing prodigiosins could be used as red tide controlling agents, where the reduction of microalgae appears within a period ranging from several hours to several days after the inoculation with most of the prodigiosin-producing bacteria (Kim et al. 2008a; Priya et al. 2013).

2. j) Anticancer and immunosuppressive properties of bacterial prodigiosins:

The anticancer and immunosuppressive properties of bacterial prodigiosins have been subject to extensive studies. It was suggested that anticancer properties of prodigiosin may have been a contributory factor in the induction of tumor necrosis and the subsequent apoptosis of cancer cells when Coley's toxins were used to treat multiple forms of cancer between 1893 and 1960 (Bennett and Bentley 2000).Overall, prodigiosins have been tested on more than 60 cancer cell lines with an average inhibitory concentration of 2 μM and confirmed potent inhibitory activity on T lymphocyte proliferation.

2. k) Anticancer activity of bacterial prodigiosins:

Prodigiosins exhibit anticancer activity by inducing apoptosis specifically in tumor cells. They were also shown to successfully target multidrug-resistant cells.

At cytotoxic concentrations, prodigiosins have been shown to interfere with different signaling pathways such as the mitogen-activated protein kinase (MAPK) signaling pathway or mitochondria cell death pathway leading to apoptosis of cancer cells. At noncytotoxic concentrations, prodigiosins prevent the cancer growth by provoking cell cycle arrest.

8

Prodigiosins can also act as DNA intercalating agents causing DNA fragmentation and tumor cell death (Melvin et al. 2000).

2. l) Immunosuppressive properties:

Prodigiosin was identified to inhibit murine T cell proliferation in vitro and in vivo at noncytotoxic concentration (Han et al. 1998 Magae *et al.*, 1996; Nakamura et al. 1986) . Due to significant toxic effects in effective doses, bacterial prodigiosins are not still clinically suitable immunosuppressants.

2. m) Bacterial prodigiosins as biocolorants:

Prior to the development of synthetic dyes, prodigiosin was used for the dyeing of silk and wool, and this has inspired the recent suggestion that prodigiosin might have utility as a multifunctional bio colorant in textile, food, and cosmetic industries (Alihosseini et al. 2008; Dufosse 2009). Prodigiosin of high purity from *S. marcescens* was previously successfully used as a colorant on different fabrics (acrylic fiber, silk, cotton, polyester, and polyester microfiber), suggesting that it can be used to dye acrylics with satisfactory color fastness (Ahmad et al. 2012; Liu *et al.*, 2013b).

2. n) Bacterial Prodigiosin applications and future developments

Bacterial prodigiosins are undisputedly multitasking molecules, but their eco physiological roles in producing organisms and possible involvement in bacterial communication still need to be elucidated. The most pronounced feature is their pharmacological activity, so further clinical developments are ongoing and needed.

In this present study focused on enhance the production of prodigiosin like pigment by media optimization and oil effluent supplementation.

3. *Serratia marcescence* –A Prodigiosin Producer:

Serratia marcescence is a gram negative, non-motile, citrate positive bacterium classified in the large family of *Enterobacteriaceae*. Serratia could be distinguished from other genera by its production of three enzymes namely, DNAase, lipase and gelatinase. Colonies on to nutrient agar are convex, circular with entire margin. *Serratia* like other Enterobacteriaceae, grow well on ordinary media under anaerobic and aerobic conditions. They grow well on synthetic media using various compounds as a single carbon source. Optimum growth of all strains of Serratia had been observed at pH 9 and at temperatures from 20–37°C. *Bacillus prodigiosus*, bacterium which was later renamed as *S. marcescens*, historically well known for "bleeding bread" As the name these compounds were thought to be responsible for a number of prodigious miracles such as the appearance of "blood" on bread and other starchy foods in the middle Ages.

4. Pigment Production:

S.marcescence was produced red color pigment called prodigiosin whereas rest does not (Kamble K.D and Hiwarale V.D, 2012). The red pigment prodigiosin was isolated from *S.marcescence* in 1902 by Kraft (Venil and Lakshmanperumalsamy, 2009). This secondary metabolite was a strong therapeutic molecule especially for their immunosuppressive properties and anticancer properties (Perez-Tomas *et al.*, 2003). The red colour pigment was also produced by other bacteria species, such as *Vibrio psychroerythrus* (Chang C-C, Chen W-C *et al.*, 2011), *S. rubidaea Pseudomonas magnesiorubra, Alteromonas rubra, and Nocardia spp.* Actinomycetes, such as *Streptoverticillium rubrireticuli* and *Streptomyces longisporus ruber* (Grimont F *et al.*,2006).*S. marcescensspecies* are the major producers of Prodigiosin (Wei-Chuan Chen *et al.*,2013, Furstner, A. 2003) .

4. Production of Prodigiosin:

The isolation and presumptive of *Serratia* in differential and selective media had been developed. Capryllate Thallous [CT] agar contains Capryllate as a carbon source for *Serratia* and Thallous salts as inhibitors for other organisms (Staunton J., Wilkinson B. 1997) and CT is the best at selecting for *Serratia*. The regular liquid media being used for prodigiosin biosynthesis was nutrient broth (Pryce L.H., Terry F.W, 2000), peptone glycerol broth (Hiroaki M., Hiroyuki A, 1996), and production medium (Staunton J., Wilkinson B, 1997).

Bacterial prodigiosin production levels are greatly influenced by nutritional and physicochemical factors, such as nitrogen and carbon sources, inorganic salts, temperature, pH, agitation, and dissolved oxygen concentration.

S. marcescens can secrete pigment, biosurfactant (Matsuyama *et al.*, 1996), and a number of extracellular enzymes such as nuclease, protease, chitinase, chitosanase, and lipase (O'Rear J *et al.*, 1992, Grimont *et al.*, 1984, Wang SL *et al.*, 2008). Pigments produced by *S. marcescens* are divided into two categories .

5. Types of Pigments:

(i). The first type, pyrimine, is a water-soluble pink pigment, which requires iron to facilitate pigment formation (Grimont PAD *et al.*, 1984); and the

(ii). Second type of Prodigiosin (Khanafari A *et al.*, 2006). Prodigiosin have a broad range of inhibitory activities against many species of bacteria, fungi and protozoa.

Having an insight on the composition of already published media the idea of designing a new, nutritious and economically cheap medium was thought of for the prodigiosin biosynthesis.

The prodigiosin pigment is a lipid based pigment. Hence many researches have been done by supplementing the production media with various kinds of lipid substrates to support pigment production. In the present study the coconut oil was tested as a lipid substrate.

In the trial for cost effective media formulation for pigment production, the heated oil already used for frying purpose and the vegetable oil mill effluent loaded naturally with oily substrates which is otherwise a waste pollutant for the environment is used in the present study. Used and heated oils from food manufacturing companies can make a cheaper source of an oil substrate. Any enhanced production in the former case could help to recycle the oil waste reject from households and cafeteria for the production of the most needed pigment in the medical and industrial field in a cost effective way. Similarly if an increased pigment production is obtained in the later case in definitely will be the most cheap way for pigment production as well as environmental protection, whereby there is no need for looking for a costly lipid source used in the human diet.

Claira *et al.*, 2014 reported that a large-scale cultivation of prodigiosin by using brown sugar was cheap for the growth of *Serratia marcescens* UTM1 and to producing red-pigment prodigiosin. the yield of prodigiosin w8000 mg l⁻¹.

Geetha *et al.*, 2014 reported that the Methanol was used for the optimized cultural conditions for the production of prodigiosin by *S. marcescence* and screening for the antimicrobial activity of prodigiosin.

Darah *et al.*, 2014 reported that the *Serratia marcescence* IBRL USM 84 isolated from the surface of a marine sponge *Xestospongia testudinaria* and the antibacterial red pigment prodigiosin production profiles from highest yield achieved at the 48 hours of cultivation (14.08 U/ml) time in marine broth when incubated at 25 °C with 150 rpm agitation.

Sumathi *et al.*, 2014 observed that the *Serratia marcescence* NPLR1 prodigiosin production was maximum obtained with Tannery fleshing (TF) which was used as both the carbon and nitrogen source in the optimized condition for maximum prodigiosin production. The optimum conditions required for the maximum prodigiosin concentration were achieved at time 30 hrs, temperature 30⁰C, pH 8, and 3% substrate concentration.

Rahul *et al.*, 2014 stated that to providing potato powder was followed by sesame and mannitol as a carbon sources and casein hydrolysate was followed by yeast and malt extract as a nitrogen sources for the Production of Prodigiosin by *Serratia marcescens*. Sweet potato powder and casein can be a potential alternative bio resource for production of pigment prodigiosin.

Heba *et al.*, 2014 reported that the ultraviolet (UV) radiation and ethyl methanesulfonate (EMS) to induce and enhance the pigmentation of *S. marcescence*. The EMS-variant (S26) produced prodigiosin eight-fold higher than that of the parent strain. Physical and chemical stress induced on *S. marcescence*, were selected and they showed different patterns in growth at 38 °C, salinity tolerance, emulsification and hemolytic activities compared to the parent *S. marcescence*.

Liang *et al.,* 2013 stated that the Serratia *marcescens*TKU011 PG on squid pen powder (SPP) medium containing phosphate and ferrous ion supplementation to produce prodigiosin production Autoclave treatment showed positive results for PG productivity (2.48 mg/mL), which increased 2.5-fold when the organism was incubated in 50 mL of 40-min autoclaved medium in a baffle-based flask (250 mL) containing 1.5% SPP at 30∘C for 1 day and then at 25∘C for 2 additional days.

Chen, *et al.,* 2013 that the Starch and peptone were identified as the optimized carbon and nitrogen sources and to improve the production of prodigiosin by *S. marcescence* C3 the prodigiosin production of 7.07 g/L was achieved when the concentrations of two trace compounds, $FeSO_4 \cdot 4H_2O$ and $MnSO_4 \cdot 4H_2O$, were optimized.

Pradeep *et al.,* 2013 stated that the natural substrates (black sesame powder, fenugreek powder, mustard oil, mustard powder, olive oil, peanut oil, peanut powder, sesame oil, and white sesame powder) for enhanced prodigiosin production from *Serratia marcescence* and they suggested that the tested substrates, peanut powder was found to be the best natural substrate at the concentration of 2% in distilled water in cost effective manner. The production was 5.2 times higher than the optimized basal medium.

Bharmal *et al.,* 2012 stated that the Prodigiosin production was induced the prodigiosin production in only by methionine or cysteine in the presence of glucose in *Serratia marcescence* MSK1 which was isolated from the air. Prodigiosin production was optimized to obtain maximum yield in M9 medium with 0.4% mannose, 0.01% Methionine, 0.003% Cysteine and 0.1% Ammonium chloride, pH 8 at 280C under shaker conditions (120rpm) for 24 hrs.

Chandrashekhar Naik *et al.*,2012 reported that the from the different agro-waste such as peanut oil cake (POC), coconut oil cake (COC), sesame oil cake (SOC), sunflower seed oil cake (SFOC) and cotton seed oil cake (CSOC), the POC was showed highly beneficial for the pigment production in *Serratia marcescens*-CF-53 through fermentation. Maximum amount of pigment was obtained (~40 mg/ml) in POC extract at 30°C for 42 hours using 8% inoculums density compared to PG broth (14.2 mg/ml). The pigment yield was almost three fold higher than that of the PG broth.

Kamble K.D and Hiwarale V.D 2012 stated that the levels of prodigiosin in peptone glycerol broth and nutrient broth and they observed that the greater levels of prodigiosin were in nutrient broth which was quite significant. They also found out that prodigiosin production was increasing gradually while the media kept for aeration and also after 48h and were maximum towards 72hrs thereafter the production was decreasing towards 92 hrs in both media.

Swiatek *et al.*, 2012 report that the increased undecylprodigiosin levels were achieved through engineering of primary metabolis and regulatory cascades controlling antibiotic production levels in *Serratia*.

James *et al.*, 2012 that the data supported a model in which the oxidation of D-glucose by quinoprotein GDH initiates a reduction in pH that inhibits prodigiosin production in *Serratia marcescence* through transcriptional control of the prodigiosin biosynthetic operon and providing new insight into the genetic pathways that control prodigiosin production. They used transposon mutagenesis to identify genes involved in the inhibition of prodigiosin by glucose.

Gulani *et al.*, 2012 were assessed that the processing parameters influencing the enhanced production of prodigiosin from *Serratia marcescence* and reported that the maximal amount of prodigiosin was produced at temperature 25 °C, pH 7.0 and incubation period of 48 hrs. The Supplementation of media with maltose and peptone yielded maximal amount of prodigiosin. Incorporation of minimal amount of supplements like silica gel, iron salts, inorganic phosphate also showed promising results.

Fang., 2011 were established an prodigiosin production by solid fermentation method to utilizing inexpensive the kitchen waste and they observed the optimum prodigiosin production was achieved when the moisture level was 200%. After modifying the fermentation conditions, the maximum prodigiosin yield was more than 4155 milligram per kilo kitchen waste at 60hrs, which was two times more than initial production yield.

Dhahi *et al.,* 2011 suggested that the in brain-heart infusion broth medium was supplemented with olive oil and casein hydrolysate as a carbon and nitrogen sources and in a concentration of 1.5% for broth, KH2PO4 as a phosphate source at initial medium to optimum for the prodigiosin production from *Serratia marcescence* S11 . the production medium were optimize the pH 8, and incubation at 28°C for 24 hours prodigiosin activity produced by *Serratia marcescence* S11 in culture medium was increased from 200 U/cell before optimization to 3000 U/cell.

Gutierrez-Roman *et al.,* 2011 reported that the potential of three *Serratia marcescens* strains (CFFSUR-B2, CFFSUR-B3 and CFFSUR-B4) isolated from tropical regions in Mexico was cultivated in oil seed based media (peanut, sesame, soybean and castor bean) and in Luria–Bertani medium which showed highest level of prodigiosin (40 µg/ml) was produced in the peanut-based medium. The amount of prodigiosin produced increased with greater inoculums densities, and the production was not affected by pH.

Chang *et al.*, 2011 reported that the, glycerol, glycine, fatty acids, and vegetable oils were found to be promising carbon sources or additives for increased prodigiosin production levels.

Antony *et al.*, 2011 reported that the optimal condition for the water-insoluble red pigment production from *Serratia marcescence* in nutrient broth was found to be at 28°C and pH 7 for 72 hrs.

Irina N. Ryazantseva *et al.*, 2011 reported that the illumination conditions (light/darkness) affected both the biosynthesis of prodigiosin and energy metabolism of the pigmented strain ATCC 9986 *Serratia marcescence*. In the process incubation the transition of the pigmented culture from illumination within (24 hrs and 48 hrs) in the dark conditions increased the prodigiosin synthesis by 2.0, 2.5 times, respectively. At the same time, the illumination did not influence the prodigiosin biosynthesis in the stationary growth phase. The regulation of energetic pathways in the light and in darkness has been revealed.

Wang *et al.*, 2011 had suggested that a potential method for developing mass production of prodigiosin from *Serratia marcescence* TKU011 using fishery-processing wastes of squid pen powder (SPP) as the sole carbon and nitrogen (C/N) sources. Fishery-processing waste (squid pen) was used to produce prodigiosin at greater quantities and they found that the prodigiosin had a novel property of insecticidal activity.

Casullo *et al.*, 2010 were indentify that the industrial wastes could be used for growth and pigment production of S. *marcescence*. They had got a highest level of prodigiosin 49.5 g/L at 48 h of cultivation using 6% "*manipueira*" .The cassava waste water was supplemented with mannitol (2%) at pH 7 and 28 °C and commented that Carbohydrates in "*manipueira*" and mannitol play a role in the enhanced cell growth and prodigiosin production.

Kalivoda *et al.*, 2010 found that the carbohydrates showed poor nutrient sources for the production of prodigiosins, with glucose as a repressor of

17

prodigiosin synthesis in *S. marcescence* via the cyclic 3'-5'-adenosine monophosphate (cAMP)-negative regulation.

Zhao *et al.,* 2009 stated thaThe mutation of *Serratia marcescens* ECU1010 by physical involving treatment by UV-irradiation for 30 sec. A mutant strain UV-01, showed enhanced lipase production, but lost the capability of producing red pigment (prodigiosin).

Sundaramoorthy *et al.,* 2009 stated that the optimized the parameters such as temperature, pH, sugar substrate and oil substrate to increase the production of prodigiosin. And they were observed that maximum amount of prodigiosin was produced at temperature 30°C and pH 7.0. Among the different sugar substrates tested maltose when amended in the medium gave higher yield than glucose, lactose and sucrose (2%) in nutrient broth. From the various oil substrates supplementation, the production of prodigiosin was maximum (535±45 mg/L) when the medium was amended with peanut oil.

Anita *et al.,* 2006 studied that the production condition, physicochemical and functional characteristics, structure, genetic and gene expression, apoptosis and toxigenic effects of prodigiosin from *Serratia marcescence.*

Yu-Hong Wei and Wei-Chuan Chen, 2005 were enhanced the production of Prodigiosin-like Pigment (PLP) from *Serratia marcescens* SMΔR by Medium Improvement and Oil-Supplementation Strategies. The PLP yield was higher in sunflower oil (6%)-supplemented Modified Luria–Bertani (MLB) medium, which resulted in an approximately 14-fold higher PLP yield than that in LB broth. Luria–Bertani (LB) was modified by increasing the concentrations of tryptone and yeast extract while completely removing NaCl from the medium.

Yu-Hong *et al.,* 2005 reported that the enhanced Undecylprodigiosin Production from *Serratia marcescence* Simon Swift-1 (SS-1) by Medium Formulation and Amino-Acid Supplementation. Among the different amino acids which containing pyrrole-like structures, proline (2.5 g l^{-1}) had highest UP production than histidine and aspartic acid in YE medium.

Taoy et al., 2005 obtained increased productivity by U.V. mutation with rational screening methods and a two-step feeding strategy from Serratia marcescens mutant. They got 2.8-fold higher prodigiosin production from mutant strain B6 than that of the parent strain with glycerol as a carbon source. Two-step feeding strategy in which glucose was selected as the initial carbon source in the fermentation media and glycerol was fed as a prodigiosin inducer, it gave a 7.8 times higher prodigiosin production (583 mg/l) than the parent stain with the original cultivation mode.

In 2005 Oller reported that the glucose and sorbitol had a repressive effect on prodigiosin synthesized by Serratia marcescence.

Anuradha et al., 2004 reported that the yield of Prodigiosin from Serratia marcescence by the addition of powdered and sieved peanut seed of different quality grades compared with the existing nutrient broth and peptone glycerol broth. Survey on the composition of the different media components in nutrient broth, peptone glycerol broth and the fatty acid containing seeds and oils enabled us to propose that the saturated form of fatty acid has a role to play in enhanced cell growth and prodigiosin production. Their work had also reported that the temperature related block of prodigiosin biosynthesis varies with different media and the powdered peanut broth supports prodigiosin production at higher temperatures.

Giri et al, 2004 were reported that the prodigiosin pigment production of Serratia marcescens in series of media and found out a novel peanut seed broth give rise to significant enhancement of prodigiosin production.

Hardjito et al., 2002 studied on Serratia marcescens biovar A2/A6 which was isolated from an Indonesian freshwater source, and they analyze the effect of carbon and nitrogen sources with the help of Placket-Burman design. Based on results of physiological and biochemical studies, the optimum conditions for growth and pigment formation were incubation 30°C in a neutral to slightly alkaline medium containing lactic acid and beef extract.

Shahitha and Poornima 2001 observed that a high pigment production in powdered peanut seed broth and powdered sesame seed broth from *Serratia marcescence* when compared to nutrient broth and peptone glycerol broth. And they also included that among different oil such as peanut oil, sesame oil and coconut oil, peanut oil showed high production.

Yamashita *et al.*, 2001 studies showed that the addition of silica-gel carriers to a liquid culture of *S. marcescens* also leads to marked increases in cell growth and the production of prodigiosin and serrawettin.

Su *et al.*, 2001 stated that an optimal concentration for peptone and inorganic phosphate for the production of prodigiosin by *S. marcescens* to the levels of 2.4 $g/^{-1}$and identified the importance of sucrose and glycine for the high production levels.

Song Cang *et al.*, 2000 reported that when *Serratia marcescence* S389 grown on ethanol and with the omission of inorganic phosphate and NaCl from the medium. 200-fold greater prodigiosin yield

Pryce and Terry 2000 suggested that the complete block in prodigiosin production from *Serratia marcescence* was observed in most of the basically used media tested at 37° C.

Kim *et al.*, 1999 worked on integrated fermentation–separation processes using a polymeric adsorbent were investigated to increase the productivity of red pigment from *Serratia* sp. KH-95. The maximal production of total pigment (6.92 g/L) was obtained when the 10% (v: v) HP-20 resin was added as a polymeric adsorbent after 10 hours. The bioreactor equipped with an extractive column packed with HP-20 adsorbent resin showed higher productivity (about 31% increment) than the conventional batch bioreactor.

Mine *et al.*, 1999 were found that Cefoxitin, erythromycin, tobramycin, co-trimoxazole, imipenem and nitrofurantoin inhibitory effect on pigmentation in a S. *marcescens* strain isolated from urine. It was also shown that the LD50 dose determined by inoculation of eight-week-old BALB/C mice with serial dilutions of overnight cultures of pigmented and nonpigmented variants was lower (LD50 = 300 X 103.94) in the nonpigmented variant than in the pigmented one (LD50 = 300 X *105 .58)*.

Feng *et al.*, 1982 reported that the addition of surfactants Sodium Dodecyl Sulphate (SDS), could also enhance the recovery efficiency for prodigiosins.

AIM:

To stimulate the production of Prodigiosin-like pigments from *Serratia marcescens*   by medium improvement methods and vegetable oil effluent supplementation.

OBJECTIVES:

- ∝ Screening for prodigiosin red pigment producing *Serratia marcescens* from the soil nearby the area where oil refinery effluent collected.

- ∝ Comparison of pigment production in normal and modified media.

- ∝ Analysis of Physico-Chemical Parameter of the Oil Effluent: pH, Temperature, Suspended Solids, Dissolved Solids and Oil Content

- ∝ Media formulation using Oil Substrate for optimizing pigment production:

- ∝ Testing of pigment production in effluent formulated media.

- ∝ Presumptive identification and confirmation of the pigment:

MATERIALS & METHODS

A. REQUIRED MATERIALS:

(i).Glass wares:

1. Test Tubes
2. Petri plates.
3. Conical Flask (different in size).
4. Pipettes and Tips.
5. Beaker.

(ii).Equipments:

1. Autoclave.
2. Laminar Air flow Chamber.
3. Micro Oven.
4. Incubator and shaker.
5. UV. Spectrophotometer.
6. Hot Air Oven.
7. Vacuum filtration Apparatus.
8. Vortex mixer.
9. Centrifuge.

(iii).Chemicals:

1. Nutrient Agar.
2. Luria Bertani broth
3. Tryptone, NaCl and Yeast Extract.
4. Nutrient Gelatin Agar.
5. Skim Milk Agar.
6. Chemicals for Biochemical test

B. METHODS:

I. Isolation and Screening of *Serratia* from Soil Sample:

Soil samples were collected from nearby the area where the oil effluent was collected (Erode, Sri Maruthi oil mill) for Screening of *Serratia sps*. The collected soil sample was serially diluted and plated on nutrient agar plates. Light red-pigmented colonies, SM-1 (Strain 1) were isolated from the plates after incubation and preserved at 4°C. A lab maintained strain SM-2 (Strain 2) also was procured from the Microbiology laboratory, Periyar University, plated and preserved for further process.

II. Identification of Bacterial Strain:

(i)Colony Morphology:

The colony color, size, texture, opacity, margination and elevation were noted.

(ii). Physical characterization of bacterial isolates:

a). Grams Staining:

A small amount of saline was placed on a clean glass slides .A thin culture smear was prepared from each strain using inoculation loop. After heat fixing of the smear few drop of crystal violet was added on both slides and allowed for one minutes. After washing the slides, Gram's iodine was added and kept for one minute. Then slides were washed properly. The smears were decolorized with alcohol (95% alcohol and 5% acetone) following washing with distilled water. Counter stain (safranin) was added and kept for 30 seconds. The slides were washed, dried and observed under oil immersion. Gram positive will show violet/purple and gram negative will show pink/red color.

b) Biochemical Characterization:

From the Gram's staining result, it was found that the strain was Gram negative short rods. so for further characterization, different bio-chemical tests were performed to identify the species of strains. For the Identification and characterization of isolate bacterial strains Bergey's manual of determinative bacteriology was used and on the basis of this manual the species was found.

Peptone broth, MR-VP broth, Simmons citrate media, Triple sugar Iron media were prepared and poured aseptically in to tubes. The isolated bacteria were inoculated in to respective medium and tubes were incubated at room temperature for 24 hrs. After incubation, Kovac's reagent, Methyl-red indicator and Barrit's reagent A and B were added to appropriate tubes and observed for the presence or absence of cherry red colour in case of indole, deep red color in the case of methyl red, deep pink color in the case of voges-proskauer and deep Prussian blue in case of citrate utilization test.

(iii). Screening for Bacterial Extra Cellular Enzyme:

a).Catalase :

The small amount of bacterial colony was transferred from agar plate to the clean dry glass slide using a wooden applicator stick. Smear was made by a drop of sterile saline. One drop of 3% hydrogen peroxide was added to the smear on the glass slide.

b).Oxidase test:

Take oxidase disc (N, N-Tetra methyl- para-phenylenediaminedihydrochloride) in a clean microscopic slide. Place one or two drops of culture on the disc. Development of blue or purple coloration was positive to oxidase production.

c). Gelatin Hydrolysis test:

The objective of the test is to determine bacterial production of gelatins enzymes that liquefy the gelatin. Pure culture was inoculated in nutrient gelatin media and then it was incubated for 24 hours at 30°C temperature .The Positive result will show the media get liquefied.

d).Nitrate Reductase Test:

The bacterial isolate were inoculated in a nitrate broth containing potassium nitrate as the sole nitrogen source. After 5 days of incubation, 1ml of 1% sulphanilamide solution and 1ml of 0.02% naphthyl-ethlene-diamine-dihydrochloride solution were added in series. The reduction of nitrate to nitrite was indicated by the appearance of red color.

d).Casien Hydrolysis: CASEIN MEDIUM (AJELLO et al, 1963; HASTINGS, 1903)

Prepare separately,

> **(i). Skim milk (dehydrated or instant nonfat milk):10g**
> **Distilled water: 100 ml**
> **(ii) .Distilled water: 100 ml**
> **Agar: 2 g.**

Prepared media was Autoclaved at 120°C for 20 minutes. Cool both solutions to about 45°C. Mix and pour into sterile petriplates. Bacteria inolulam were seeded on the skim milk agar by point inoculation. The cultures were incubated for 24 hours at room temperature and then examined for evidence of casein hydrolysis (William *et al.,* 1972).

III. Bacterial Growth in Luria Bertani Broth:

(i). LB₁ ➡ Coventional LB broth medium.

Tryptone   = 1.g/100 ml.

Yeast Extract = 0.5.g/100ml.

NaCl   = 1.g/100ml.

(ii).LB₂ ➡ Modified LB broth (MLB) amended with increased Tryptone composition.

Tryptone   = 2.g/100 ml.

Yeast Extract = 0.5.g/100ml.

NaCl   = 1.g/100ml.

(iii).LB₃ ➡ Modified LB broth (MLB) amended with lack of Nacl composition.

Tryptone   = 1.g/100 ml.

Yeast Extract = 0.5.g/100ml.

IV. Pigment Production Analysis:

(i). Extraction of prodigiosin

The cells were harvested by centrifugation at 10,000 rpm for 10 min. The supernatant was discarded and the pellet was resuspended in acidified ethanol (4% of 1M HCL in 96 ml ethanol). The mixture was vortexed and the suspension was centrifuge at 10,000 rpm for 10 min. The supernatant prodigiosin was transferred to the fresh vial (Slater *et al.*, 2003).

(ii). Estimation of prodigiosin:

The absorption pattern over various wavelengths was initially checked and it was found that the absorption maxima were at 499nm where prodigiosin also absorbs maximally. At this wavelength the absorptions were recorded.

Isolated prodigiosin was estimated using the following formula (Mekhael and Yousif, 2009).

$$\text{Prodigiosin unit/cell} = \left\{ \frac{[OD_{499} - (1.381 \times OD_{620})] \times 1000}{OD_{620}} \right\}$$

Where,

OD $\longrightarrow$ Optical density.

OD_{499} $\longrightarrow$ Pigment absorbance.

OD_{620} $\longrightarrow$ Bacterial cell absorbance.

1.381 $\longrightarrow$ Constant.

V. Physico - Chemical Parameter of the Oil Effluent:

1. Physical Parameters:

(i). PH of the Oil Effluent:

pH of the oil effluent was checked using pH meter.

(ii). Temperature:

Temperature is the degree of hotness or coldness of a substance. The apparatus used for the measurement was mercury thermometer (Borosil). The thermometric bulb containing the mercury was vertically immersed in the effluent and allowed to stand for some minutes till the temperature reading was steady before obtaining reading (Olaniyi *et al.*, 2012)

(iii).Total Solids (TS):

A clean dish of suitable size was dried at $103-105^0C$ in an oven until a constant weight was obtained. It was subsequently cooled to room temperature in and later weighed.100ml sample was measured into a dish and evaporated to dryness on a steam bath. The outside of the dish was wiped and the residue was dried in an oven for 1 hour at $103-105°C$. The dish was kept for cooled to room temperature and weighed. The dish was dried further in an oven for 10-20 minutes, reweighed after cooling to room temperature. This was repeated until the weight of the dish plus residue was constant to within 0.05mg (Olaniyi *et al.*, 2012).

(iv). Total Suspended Solids (TSS):

Filter paper was taken and dried to a constant weight. Then it was cooled in to room temperature in a dessicator and the weight was noted. The fiber paper was placed into the funnel carefully with the aid of a pair of tongs. The oil effluent sample was thoroughly mixed with a stirrer, after which 100ml was quickly measured into the filtering apparatus. After filtration elapsed, the filter paper was carefully taken out from the funnel and then dried to a constant weight at $103-105°C$. The weight was noted (Olaniyi *et al.*, 2012).

(v). Total Dissolved Solids (TDS):

A measured volume of oil effluent (100.ml) was taken in a vial and stirred properly. Oil effluent was taken in to the vacuum apparatus with whatsmann filter paper and applied vacuum pressure. It was washed with three successive 10ml volumes of distilled water, allowing complete drainage between washings, and suction was continued for 3 minutes after filtration was completed. Total filtrate with washings was transferred to weigh evaporating dish and evaporated to dryness on a steam bath. Evaporated sample was dried in the oven for 1 hour at $180 \pm 2^{0}C$, cooled in room temperature and weighed (Olaniyi *et al.,* 2012).

(vi). Oil Content by Gravimetric Method:

Gravimetric-based methods measure anything extractable by a solvent that is not removed during a solvent evaporation process and is capable of being weighed. The sample was acidified previously (1:1) HCL to pH<2 or lower (generally, 5ml is sufficient for 1 liter sample).). 100ml of sample was transferred to a separating funnel followed by the addition of 300ml n-hexane. Oil from the Sample was extracted by a solvent. It was shaken vigorously for 30 minutes for the layers to separate. The n-hexane layer (now containing oil) was drained through a funnel into a flask, which has been weighed beforehand. The flask is placed into a temperature controlled water bath, and the solvent is evaporated at a specific temperature, condensed and collected. After the solvent is evaporated, the flask now containing the residual oil is dried and weighed. Knowing the weight of the empty flask, the amount of residual oil can be calculated (Ming Yang, 2011).

VI. Media formulation using Oil Substrate for optimizing pigment production:

The optimized factors were included in LB media that were found by the earlier methods and adopted for the further experiments. The optimized LB media was treated with different oil substrate to check for prodigiosin pigment production from *Serratia*. The oil substrates used were raw coconut oil and cooked coconut oil. The concentration of oil was kept uniform in the 2 treatment.

(i)   Raw Oil Treated Media **(ROTM)** ;optimized LB Medium with 4% of raw oil supplementation

(ii) Cooked coconut Oil Treated Media **(COTM)**; optimized LB Medium with 4% of Cooked coconut Oil supplementation.

VII. Testing of Pigment Production in Raw Oil Effluent:

❖ Addition of natural oil mill effluent was also used in place of optimized LB media.

❖ Effluent Oil Treated media **(EOTM)**; optimized LB Medium with oil effluent.

100ml of Oil effluent was taken in conical flask instead of distilled water. The optimized composition of LB medium (LB$_3$) was added in to the measured oil effluent. After Sterilization the media kept for cooled done to room temperature and culture was inoculated. Incubated at room temperature.

VIII. Quantification of the prodigiosin-like pigment:

The culture broth (0.5 ml) was mixed with an equal volume of 2% (w/v) alum placed in a vial. Four milliliters of methanol was added to the vial and the mixture was vigorously vortexed with the help of vortex mixer. The solution was then centrifuged at 1200 rpm for 10 min. A fixed amount (0.8 ml) of the supernatant was further mixed with 0.2 ml of 0.05 N HCl/methanol mixture (4:1

[v/v]) (Yu-Hong Wei and Wei-Chuan Chen, 2005). The optical density of the resulting solution was measured. The absorption pattern over various wave lengths was initially checked and it was found that the absorption maxima were at 499nm where prodigiosin also absorbs maximally. At this wavelength the absorptions were recorded. Isolated prodigiosin was estimated using the following formula (Mekhael and Yousif. 2009).

$$\text{Prodigiosin unit/cell} = \left\{ \frac{[OD_{499} - (1.381 \times OD_{620})] \times 1000}{OD_{620}} \right\}$$

Where,

OD $\longrightarrow$ Optical density.

OD_{499} $\longrightarrow$ Pigment absorbance.

OD_{620} $\longrightarrow$ Bacterial cell absorbance.

1.381 $\longrightarrow$ Constant.

IX. Presumptive Identification and confirmation of the pigment:

A loop full of inoculums was aseptically inoculated into 50ml nutrient broth. The flask was kept in a shaker incubator at 120rpm for 18 hours at 30°C. After incubation, the culture broth was centrifuged at 10,000 rpm for 10 minutes at room temperature. The supernatant was discarded and the pellet at the base of the centrifuge tube was suspended in equal amount of 95% of methanol and centrifuged for 10 minutes at 10,000 rpm. The supernatant was then divided into two portions. One part was acidified with a drop of concentrated HCl and the other part was alkalinized with a drop of concentrated ammonia solution. A red or pink color in the acidified solution and a yellow or tan color in the alkaline solution indicate a positive presumptive test for Prodigiosin (Ding MJ and Williams RP,1983).

I. Identification of the Bacterial strains:

The soil inoculated nutrient agar plates after 24 hrs of incubation were observed for the growth of the colonies. Among the different morphologically characterized colonies observed, a light red colored colony was selected for further screening process. Pigment production was confirmed by cultivating in the LB broth, which is taken as SM-1. The lab maintained culture was named as SM-1.

II. Morphological and biochemical characteristics of *Serratia* sp.

Characteristics	SM-1	SM-2
Gram Staining	-ve	-ve
Cell type	Short rods	Short rods
Motility test	+ve	+ve
Glucose	+ve	+ve
Lactose	-ve	-ve
Sucrose	+ve	+ve
Maltose	+ve	+ve
Indole test	- ve	- ve
Methyl red test	-ve	-ve
Voges-proskauer test	+ve	+ve
Citrate test	+ve	+ve
Oxidase test	-ve	-ve
Catalase test	+ve	+ve
Starch hydrolysis test	-ve, lack of a zone of clearing	-ve,lack of zone of clearing
Gelatin hydrolysis	+ve	+ve
Nitrate reduction test	+ve	+ve
Casein Hydrolysis	-ve	-ve

Table-1: Morphological and biochemical characteristics of *Serratia* sp

Colony Morphology: Colonies on nutrient agar were observed as convex, circular with entire margin with characteristic blood red colored pigments. The pigmentation showed by soil strain was lighter than the Lab strain. Saline emulsifications on the colony when placed on a clean grease free glass slide showed Wetting activity indicating a confirmatory test for *Serratia marcescens* sps.

The selected bacterial isolate was identified as *Serratia* sp. based on morphological and biochemical characteristics.

III: *Serratia* Growth in Luria-Bertani Broth and Pigment Production Analysis:

SM- 1 showed light pigment production than the SM- 2 in all LB media broths. The tryptone enriched medium showed greater production than normal LB broth. The production was highest in Sodium chloride devoid LB broth.

Table-2: Pigment production by the strains in different formulated media.

Media	SM-1			SM-2		
	OD_{499}	OD_{620}	Prodigiosin Unit/cell, mg/L	OD_{499}	OD_{620}	Prodigiosin Unit/cell, mg/L
LB_1	0.223	0.041	4058.024	0.246	0.032	6306.5
LB_2	0.145	0.025	4419	1.047	0.093	7152.66
LB_3	0.489	0.060	6769	0.547	0.060	7735.66

V. Physico - Chemical Parameter of the Oil Effluent:

The results of the Physico - chemical parameter of the oil effluent namely pH, Temperature, Suspended Solids, Dissolved Solids and Oil Content were given in Table- 3.

Table-3: Physico - chemical parameter of the oil effluent

PARAMETERS	UNIT	VALUE	FEPA(Tolerance Limit)
PH	-	7	6-9
Temperature	^0C	28	40
Total Solids, TS	Mg/ L	720	NS
Suspended Solids, TSS	Mg/L	400	30
Dissolved Solids, TDS	MG/L	320	2000
Oil Content	MG/L	2.4	10-30

VI. Media Optimization Using Oil Substrate:

Media	SM-1			SM-2		
	OD_{499}	OD_{620}	Prodigiosin Unit/cell, mg/L	OD_{499}	OD_{620}	Prodigiosin Unit/cell, mg/L
LB$_1$	0.729	0.477	147.301	0.065	0.014	3261.871
ROTM	0.644	0.249	1205.345	0.942	0.019	972.145
COTM	1.215	0.697	362.185	0.971	0.79	729.773

VII. Testing of Pigment Production in Raw Oil Effluent:

Media	SM-1			SM-2		
	OD_{499}	OD_{620}	Prodigiosin Unit/cell, mg/L	OD_{499}	OD_{620}	Prodigiosin Unit/cell, mg/L
LB_1	0.729	0.477	147.301	0.065	0.014	3261.871
EOTM	1.218	0.433	1431.933	0.061	0.013	3311.3077

IX. Identification of the pigment:

A red or pink color in the acidified solution and a yellow or tan color in the alkaline solution indicate a positive presumptive test for Prodigiosin (Ding *et al*, 1983). The pigment extracted from the isolated S.*marcescens* and the Lab maintained strain turned red in the acidified solution and yellow in the alkaline solution indicating a positive presumptive test for Prodigiosin.

Biopigments produced by bacteria possess enormous efficiency as medicinally important products.Prodigiosin, a red pigment, belongs to the family of tripyrrole was found to exhibit antibacterial, Antitrypanosomal, Antialgal, biocolorants, antimycotic, immunomodulating, anti-tumor and anti-malarial properties. These pigments were found associated with the cell wall vesicle of the bacteria. The present investigation centered on isolation of prodigiosin producing organisms from soil and formulating a production medium for effective production of prodigiosin.

All of the other prodigiosin-producing bacteria that have been reported used expensive materials as the C/N source for prodigiosin production and generated low amounts of prodigiosin Wei YH *et al.*, 2005.

The strains were both found to be negative to casein hydrolysis, in contrast to the earlier iochemical test reports for Serratia. The casein hydrolysis is related to the Serratapeptase (SRP) production by the organism. Absences of the hydrolytic activity probably suggest that these strains lack the production of SRP. There are reports that Serratia strains produce prodigiosin and SRP in differential concentrations according to a particular cultural condition.

Progigiosin producing bacteria elaborated the pigment at 30°C and the rate was reduced as the temperature increases. Williams & Hussain Quadri (1980) reported that no prodigiosin was produced when cultures were incubated at 38°C; however pigment production was observed when the temperature was shifted to 27°C. A complete block in prodigiosin was observed in most of the basically used media tested at 37°C was similar to the result observed by Pryce& Terry (2000).

Optical density of the prodigiosin was estimated in different modified LB media with conventional LB media. From the preliminary screening of media composition was carried out , fount out that the   Prodigiosin production was higher in the media lack of sodium chloride, Prodigiosin unit per cell in that media   was   found   to   be   7735.66,which   was   determined   by spectrophotometrically at 499nm (Mekhael and Yousif, 2009). As the same way prodigiosin in the media in which tryptone level was increased, this was found 7152.66 prodigiosin per unit cell. In normal LB composition it was 6306.5.

The inhibitory effect of the salt was most pronounced when compared to the supportive or enhancement effect of tryptone for the pigment production. There were reports already that the nitrogen sources given in the form of sodium nitrate were inhibitory for the pigment production but increased the production when nitrogen was supplied in other forms like ammonium nitrate. Also in a study made by Yu-Hong Wei *et al.*, 2005, an increment in the concentration of sodium chloride salt had greatly reduced the prodigiosin pigment production. Hence it can be concluded that sodium chloride is rather inhibitory to pigment production process by *Serratia marcesens* growth than being a osmotic regulator in the growth medium. The organism growth too was not suppressed in the absence of sodium chloride indicating that organism might possess alternative mechanisms to maintain osmotic balance.

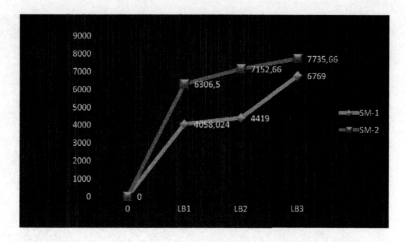

According to (kim et al., 1998). Oil gave a better yield over the various carbon (not fatty acid containing seeds) and nitrogen sources tested. The bonded fatty acids as carbon source are less accessible by *Serratia marcescens*.

A difference in species level is suspected since both the *Serratia* organisms differed in the production level of pigment in the media formulations used in the study. There was also difference in the way of utilizing substrates which suggest a metabolic difference and physiological nature among the strains used. Giri *et al.*, (2004) reported peanut seed powder increased the production of prodigiosin and they have concluded that the saturated form of fatty acid plays a role in enhanced cell growth and prodigiosin production.

Among two different oils substrate, the raw oil gave high pigment production (1205.35m/ L from SM-1 and 972.145 mg/L fro SM-2) followed by used or cooked coconut oil (362.185 mg/L from SM-1 and 729.773mg/L from SM-2).

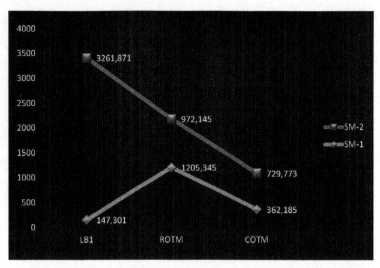

The modified LB with oil mill effluent gave increased production of prodigiosin red pigment(than other oil supplementation. This study demonstrated a feasible and effective fermentation strategy that resulted in a marked enhancement of the production of a PLP from *S. marcescens*.

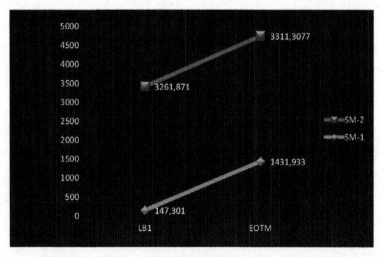

There is evidence indicating that the type of carbon source may play a crucial role in the PLP production by S. marcescens species (11). It was found that glucose may inhibit prodigiosin production due to catabolic repression (Giri *et al.*, 2004) or by lowering the medium pH (Sole *et al.*, 1997).

As a consequence, glycerol was used as a glucose alternative in a peptone glycerol broth, resulting in a better yield of prodigiosin (Montaner., 2000). A variety of plant seed oils have also been used as carbon substrates for prodigiosin production and displayed stimulatory effects on the production of prodigiosin by *S.marcescens* (Giri *et al.*, 2000). Therefore, we investigated the effect of oil substrates on the production of prodigiosin in *S. marcescens*. Therefore, investigated the effect of oil substrates on the production by choosing three inexpensive oil substrate .

SUMMARY

Bacteria isolated from the soil collected from the area where the oil mill effluent was taken, and laboratory maintained cultures were used for the present study. Among the two isolate, that is SM-1 and SM-2, the strain got from the lab was recognized to produce red pigment abundantly than the strain isolated from the soil. For the Identification and characterization of isolate bacterial strains Bergey's manual of determinative bacteriology was used and on the basis of this manual the species was predicted as *Serratia*.

Luria-Bertani media was optimized by changing their media compositions. And the optimized media was used for the further different oil substrate supplementation process. After estimating the prodigiosin production in that modified media LB_3 found out that the optimized pigment production.

Oil supplementation was given to optimized media such as Raw Oil, cooked oil and oil effluent. In the case of raw oil substrate both the strain gave higher production than the ordinary media. But in the case of cooked oil both gave lesser compared to the ordinary one.

Oil mill effluent modified media gave higher production compared to the other oil substrate. The pigment obtained from in this study likely to be Prodigiosin got by presumptive test and identified.

Alihosseini F,Ju KS, Lango J,Hammock BD,Sun G. 2008. Antibacterial colorants:characterization of prodiginines and their applications on textile materials. *Biotechnol Prog.*, 24:742–7.

Alihosseini, F., Ju, K-S., Lango, J., Hammock, BD and Sun, G. 2008. Antibacterial colorants: characterization of prodiginines and their applications on textile materials. *Biotechnol Prog.*, 24:742–747.

Anita Khanafari., Mahnaz Mazaheri Assadi and Fatemeh Ahmadi Fakhr. 2006. Review of Prodigiosin, Pigmentation in *Serratia marcescens*. *Online Journal of Biological Scie* 6 (1): 1-13.

Antony, V.S., Chandana, K, Senthilkumar, P and Narendra Kumar, G. 2011. Optimization of prodigiosin production by *Serratia marcescens* SU-10 and evaluation of its bioactivity. *Inter Research Journal of Biotech.*,2(5):128-133.

Anuradha V Giri., Nandini Anandkumar., Geetha Muthukumaran and Gautam Pennathur. 2004. A novel medium for the enhanced cell growth and production of prodigiosin from *Serratia marcescens* isolated from soil. *BMC Microbiology.*, 4:11.

Azambuja, P., Feder, D and Garcia, ES. 2004. Isolation of *Serratia marcescens* in the mid gut of Rhodnius prolixus: impact on the establishment of the parasite Trypanosoma cruzi in the vector. *Exp Parasitol.*, 107:89–96.

Azuma, T., Watanabe, N., Yagisawa, H., Hirata, H., Iwamura, M., and Kobayashi, Y. 2000. Induction of apoptosis of activated murine splenic T cells by cycloprodigiosin hydrochloride, a novel immunosuppressant. *Immunopharmacology.*, 46: 29–37.

Beatriz, M., Navarro, S., Pique, M., Vilaseca, M., Martinell, M., Giralt, E., Gil, J and Peroz-Tomas, R. 2000. Prodigiosin from the supernatant of *Serratia marcescens* induce apoptosis in haematopoietic cancer cell lines. *Brit. J .Pharmacol.*, 131: 585-593.

Bennett, JW and Bentley, R. 2000. Seeing red: the story of prodigiosins. *Adv Appl Microbiol .,* 47:1–32.

Carbonell, T., Della Colleta HHM., Yano, T., Darini ALC, Levy, CE and Fonseca, BAL. 2000. Clinical relevance and virulence factors of pigmented *Serratia marcescens*. A low frequency of isolation of pigmented *Serratia marcescens* from clinical specimens, indicating that non pigmented strains are clinically more significant. *FEMS Immunol Microbiol Mtds.*,28(2):143-149.

Castro, AJ . 1967. Antimalarial activity of prodigiosin. *Nature.*, 213: 903–904.

Chandni Gulani., Sourav Bhattacharya and Arijit Das. 2012 Assessment of process parameters influencing the enhanced production of prodigiosin from *Serratia marcescens* and evaluation of its antimicrobial, antioxidant and dyeing potentials. *Malaysian J of Microbio.*, 8(2.):116-122.

Chandrashekar, N.,Srisevita, JM., Shushma, KN., Noorin, F., Shilpa, AC., Muttanna, CD., Darshan, N and Sannadurappa, D.2012. Peanut oil cake: A novel substrate for enhanced cell growth and prodigiosin production from *Serratia marcescence* CF-53. *Int scientific research J.*, 2(6):549-557.

Chang, C-C., Chen, W-C., Ho, S-F., Wu, H-S and Wei, Y-H. 2011. Development of natural anti-tumor drugs by microorganisms. *J Biosci Bioeng.*, 111: 501–511.

Chang-Ho, Kim., Seung-Wook, Kim and Suk-In, Hong. 1999. An integrated fermentation separation process for the production of red pigment by *Serratia* sp. KH-95. *Process Biochemistry.*,35: 485-490.

Claira Arul Aruldass., Chidambaran Kulandaisamy Venil., Zainul Akmar Zakaria and Wan Azlina Ahmad. 2014. Brown sugar as a low-cost medium for the production of prodigiosin by locally isolated *Serratia marcescens* UTM1.*Int Biodeterioration &Biodegradation.*, 95:19-24.

Clements-Jewery S. 1976. The reversal of glucose repressed prodigiosin production in *Serratia marcescens* by the cyclic 3'5'-adenosine monophosphate inhibitor theophylline. *Experientia* 32:421–422.

Darah Ibrahim., Teh Faridah Nazari., Jain Kassim and Sheh-Hong Lim. 2014. Prodigiosin - an antibacterial red pigment produced by *Serratia marcescens* IBRL USM 84 associated with a marine sponge *Xestospongia testudinaria. J Applied Pharm Scie .*,4 (10): 001-006.

Dauenhauer, S. A., Hull, R. A. and Williams, R. P. 1984. Cloning and expression in *Escherichia coli* of *Serratia marcescens* genes encoding prodigiosin biosynthesis. *J Bacteriol.*, 158: 1128–1132.

Demain, AL. 1995. In fifty years of antimicrobials: past perspectives and future trends (Eds. Hunter PA, Darby, GK & Russel, NJ), *Soc. for Gen. Microbiol.*,. 205-228.

Ding, MJ and Williams, RP. 1983. Biosynthesis of prodigiosin by white strains of *Serratia marcescens* isolated from patients. *Journal of Clinical Microbio.*, 17: 476–480.

Elahian, F., Moghimi, B., Dinmohammadi, F., Ghamghami, M., Hamidi, M and Mirzaei, SA. 2013. The anticancer agent prodigiosin is not a multidrug resistance protein substrate. *DNA Cell Biol.*, 32:90–97.

Fang Xu., Shunxiang Xia and Qiyin Yang. 2011. Strategy for Obtaining Inexpensive Prodigiosin Production by *Serratia marcescence. Biological and Environmental Eng. IPCBEE.,* vol 20.

Fürstner, A .2003 .Chemistry and biology of roseophilin and the prodigiosin alkaloids. A survey of the last 2500 years. *Chem.Int. Ed. Engl.*, 42: 3582-3603.

Furstner, A B. 2003.Chemistry and biology of roseophilin and the prodigiosin alkaloids: a survey of the last 2500 years. *Angew.Chem. Int. Ed.*, 42: 3582–3603.

Geetha Ramani, D., Amritha Nair and Krithika, K. 2014. Optimization of cultural conditions for the production of prodigiosin by *Serratia marcescence* and screening for the antimicrobial activity of prodigiosin. *Int J Pharm Bio Sci.*, 5 (3) : (B) 383 – 392.

Genes, C., Baquero, E., Echeverri, F., Maya, JD and Triana, O. 2011. Mitochondrial dysfunction in Trypanosoma cruzi: the role of *Serratia marcescens* prodigiosin in the alternative treatment of Chagas disease. Parasites Vectors., 4:66.

Genes, C., Baquero, E., Echeverri, F., Maya, JD and Triana, O. 2011. Mitochondrial dysfunction in*Trypanosoma cruzi*: the role of *Serratia* *marcescens* prodigiosin in the alternative treatment of Chagas disease. Parasites Vectors 4:66.

Gerber, NN. 1975. Prodigiosin-like pigments. *CRC Crit Rev Microbiol* ., 1975:469–485

Gerber, NN. 1975b. Prodigiosin-like pigments. CRC Crit Rev Microbiol 1975:469–485.

Giri, A., V. Nandkumar, N., Muthukumaran, G and Pennathur, G. 2004. A novel medium for the enhanced cell growth and production of prodigiosin from *Serratia marcescens* isolated from soil. *BMC Microbiol.*, 4:1–10.

Goldschmitt, M. C. and Williams, R. P .1968.Thiamin induced formation of the monopyrrole moiety of prodigiosin. *J. Bacteriol.*, 96: 609–616.

Grimont PAD and Grimont, F. 1984. In: Krieg NR, editor. Bergey's manual of systematic bacteriology, vol. 1. Baltimore, USA: Willams & Wilkins., p. 477–84.

Han, SB., Kim, HM., Kim, YH., Lee, CW., Jang, ES., Son, KH., Kim, SU and Kim, YK. 1998. T-cell specific immunosuppression by prodigiosin isolated from *Serratia marcescens. Int J Immunopharmacol.*, 20:1–13.

Heba, A., El-Bialy., Salwa, A and Abou El-Nour.2014. Physical and chemical stress on *Serratia marcescens* and studies on prodigiosin pigment production. *Ann Microbiol.*, DOI 10.1007/s13213-014-0837-8.

Helvia W. Casullo de Araúj., K. Fukushima and Galba M.Campos Takaki. 2010. Prodigiosin Production by *Serratia marcescens* UCP 1549 Using Renewable-Resources as a Low Cost Substrate.*Molecules.*, 15: 6931-6940.

Hiroaki, M., Hiroyuki, A., Masakatsu, F., Takeji, S and Teisuya, T. 1996. Industrial production of optically active intermediate in the synthesis of dialtizem with lipase. *Seibutsu kogaku.*,74: 273-288.

Irina, N. Ryazantseva., Vladimir, S. Saakov., Irina, N. Andreyeva., Tatjana, I. Ogorodnikova and Yuriy, F. Zuev. 2012. Response of pigmented *Serratia marcescens* to the illumination. *Journal of Photochemistry and Photobiology B: Biology* 106:18–23.

Isra'a M. Dhahi., Hameed M. Jasim., Abdulkareem Jasim. 2011. Optimum conditions for Prodigiosin production by *Serratia marcescens* S11. *Int J Biotech Research Center.*, vol No 5(3).

James, E. Fender., Cody, M. Bender., Nicholas, A. Stella., Roni, M. Lahr., Eric, J. Kalivoda and Robert, M. Q. Shanks. 2012. *Serratia marcescens* Quinoprotein Glucose Dehydrogenase Activity Mediates Medium Acidification and Inhibition of Prodigiosin Production by Glucose. *Applied and Environ Microbio.*, Vol.78(17).

Jin-li Tao., Xue-dong Wang., Ya-ling Shen and Dong-zhi Wei. 2005. Strategy for the improvement of prodigiosin production by a *Serratia marcescens* mutant through fed-batch fermentation.*World Journal of Micro& Biotech.*, 21: 969–972.

Jones, JDG., Grady, KL., Suslow, TV and Bedbrook, JR .1986. Isolation and characterization of genes encoding two chitinase enzymes from *Serratia marcescens. EMBO J.,* 5:467–473.

Jungdon, B., Hyunsoo, M., Kyeong-Keun, O., Chang-Ho, K., Dae SL., Seung WK and Suk-In H. 2001. A novel bioreactor with an internal adsorbent for intergrated fermentation and recovery of prodigiosin like pigment produced from *Serratia* sp. *Biotechnol Letts.*, 23:1315-1319.

Kalivoda, EJ., Stella, NA., Aston, MA., Fender, JE., Thompson, PP., Kowalski, RP and Shanks, RM . 2010. Cyclic AMP negatively regulates prodigiosin production *by Serratia marcescens. Res Microbiol.,* 161:158–167.

Kamble, K.D and Hiwarale, V.D. 2012. Prodigiosin production from *Serratia marcescens* strains obtained from farm soil. *Inter J Environmental science.*, vol.3(1).

Khanafari, A., Assadi, MM and Fakhr, FA. 2006. Review of prodigiosin, pigmentation in *S.marcescens*. *Online J Biol Sci.*, 6:1–13.

Kim, C. H., Kim, S. W., and Hong, S. I.1999.An integrated fermentation–separation process for the production of red pig ment by *Serratia* spp. KH-95. *Process Biochem.*, 35: 485–490.

Kim, D., Kim, JF., Yim, JH., Kwon, SK., Lee, Ch and Lee, HK. 2008. Red to red—the marine bacterium *Hahella chejuensis* and its product prodigiosin for mitigation of harmful algal blooms. J *Microbiol Biotechnol* ., 18:1621–1629.

Kobayashi, N and Ichikawa, Y. 1991. Separation of the prodigiosin localizing crude vesicles which retain the activity of protease and nuclease in *Serratia marcescens*. *Microbiol Immunol.*, 35:607-614.

Lawanson, A. O and Sholeye, F. O. 1975. Inhibition of prodigiosin formation in Serratia marcescensby adenosine triphosphate. Experientia, 32: 439–440.

Li-Li Zhao., Xiao-Xia Chen and Jian-He Xu. 2009. Strain improvement of *Serratia marcescens* ECU1010 and medium cost reduction for economic production of lipase. *World J Microbiol Biotechnol.*, 26:537–543.

Linawati Hardjito., Anwar Huq., and Rita R. Colwell. 2002. The Influence of Environmental Conditions on the Production of Pigment by *Serratia marcescens*. *Biotechnol. Bioprocess Eng.*, 7: 100-104.

Madhura Nerurkara., Jyoti Vaidyanathanb., Ravindra Adivarekara., Zarine Bhathena Langdanab. Use of natural dye from *Serratia marcescence* subspecies *marcescence* in dyeing of textile fabrics.

Mahajan, DM., Masand, VH., Patil, KN., Hadda, TB., Jawarkar, RD., Thakur, SD and Rastija, V. (2012) CoMSIA and POM analyses of anti-malarial activity of synthetic prodiginines. *Bioorg Med Chem Lett.,* 22:4827– 4835

Mahajan, DT., Masand, VH., Patil, KN., Hadda, TB and Rastija, V. 2013. Integrating GUSAR and QSAR analyses for antimalarial activity of synthetic prodiginines against multi drug resistant strain. *Med Chem Res.,* 22:2284–2292.

Martha Ingrid Gutierrez-Roman and Francisco Holguin-Melendez., Ricardo Bello-Mendoza• Karina Guillen-Navarro., Michael F. Dunn and Graciela Huerta-Palacios. 2012. Production of prodigiosin and chitinases by tropical *Serratia marcescens* strains with potential to control plant pathogens. *World J Microbiol Biotechnol .,* 28:145–153.

Matsuyama T and Nakagawa Y. 1996. Bacterial wetting agents working in colonization of bacteria on surface environments. *Colloids Surf B Biointerfaces.,* 7:207–14.

Matsuyama, T., Murakami, T., Fujita, M., Fujita, S and Yano, I.1986. Extracellular vesicle formation and biosurfactant production by *Serratia marcescens. J General Microbiol.,*132:865-875.

McRary, WL., Beaver, EL and Noble, ER. 1953. In vitro effects of prodigiosin and other antibiotics on Trypanosoma cruzi. *Exp Parasitol.,* 2:125–128.

Mekhael, R and Yousif, S.Y. (2009). The role of red pigment produced by *Serratia marcescens* as antibacterial and plasmid curing agent, *Journal of Duhok University.,*12 (1): 268-274.

Melvin, MS., Tomlinson, JT., Saluta, GR., Kucera, GL., Lindquist, N and Manderville, RA. 2000. Double-strand DNA cleavage by copper prodigiosin. *J Am Chem Soc.,* 122:6333–6334.

Meschke, H,. Walter, S and Schrempf, H. 2012. Characterization and localization of prodiginines from Streptomyces lividans suppressing Verticillium dahliae in the absence or presence of Arabidopsis thaliana. *Environ Microbiol* .,14:940–952.

Mine Ang-Kiii iker., Ozden Biiyiikbaba-Boral., Veniis Tolun., Didem Toriimkiiney., Serdar Sus ever and Ozdem, Ang. 1999. Effect of Some Antibiotics on Pigmentation in *Serratia marcescens. Zent.bl. Bakteriol.* 289: 781-785.

Ming Yang. 2011. Measurement of Oil in Produced Water. *Springer Science+Business Media.*

Min-Jung, Song., Jungdon Bae., Dae-Sil Lee., Chang-Ho Kim., Jun-Seok Kim., Seung-Wook Kim., and Suk-In Hong.2006. Purification and Characterization of Prodigiosin Produced by Integrated Bioreactor from *Serratia* sp. KH-95. *J Bioscience and Eng.*, 101(2): 157-161.

Mohammed Husain Bharmal, Naseer Jahagirdar and Aruna, K. 2012. Study on optimization of prodigiosin production by *Serratia marcescence*MSK1 isolated from air. *I.J.A.B.R.*, 2(4): 671-680.

Monreal, J., Reese, ET. 1969. The chitinase of *Serratia marcescens. Can J Microbiol* .,15:689–696.

Montaner, B., Navarro, S., Pique, M., Vilaseca, M., Martinell, M., Giralt, E., Gil, J and Perez-Tomas, R. 2000. Prodigiosin from supernatant of *Serratia marcescens* induces apoptosis in haematopoietic cancer cell lines. *British Journal of Pharmacology* ., 131:585-593.

Moraes, CS., Seabra, SH., Castro, DP., Brazil, RP., de Souza, W., Garcia, ES and Azambuja, P. 2008. Leishmania (Leishmania) chagasi interactions with *Serratia marcescens*: ultrastructural studies, lysis and carbohydrate effects. *Exp Parasitol.*, 118:561–568.

Nobutaka, S., Masami, N., Kazuyuki,H., Tadaaki, H and Katsumi, A. 2001. Synergistic antifungal activity of chitinolytic enzymes and prodigiosin produced by biocontrol bacterium, *Serratia marcescens* strain B2 against gray mold pathogen, Botrytis cinerea. *J Gen Plant Patho.*, 67(4):312-319.

O'Rear J, Alberti L, Harshey RM. 1992. Mutations that impair swarming motility in *S. marcescens* 274 include but not limited to those affecting chemotaxis or flagellar function. *J Bacteriol.*, 174:6125–37.

Olaniyi, Ibrahim,Raphael, Odoh and Nwadiogbu, J. Onyebuch. 2012. Effect of Industrial Effluent on the Surrrounding Environment. *Archives of Appli Scie Research.*, 4 (1):406-413.

Pandey, R., Chander, R., and Sainis, K. B. 2003.A novel prodigiosin-like immunosuppressant from an alkalophilic Micrococcussp. *Int. Immunopharmacol.*, 3: 159–167.

Papireddy, K., Smilkstein, M., Kelly, JX., Salem ,SM., Alhamadsheh, M., Haynes, SW., Challis, GL and Reynolds, KA. 2011. Antimalarial activity of natural and synthetic prodiginines. *J Med Chem.*, 54:5296–5306.

Patil, CD., Patil, SV., Salunke, BK and Salunkhe, RB. 2012. Prodigiosin produced by *Serratia marcescens* NMCC46 as a mosquito larvicidal agent against Aedes aegypti and Anopheles stephensi. *Parasitol Res.*, 109:1179–1187.

Pérez-Tomás, R and Viñas, M., 2010. New insights on the antitumoral properties of prodiginines. *Curr. Med. Chem.,* 17: 2222–2231.

Pradeep, B.V., Stanly Pradeep, F., Angayarkanni, J and Palaniswamy, M. 2013. Cost Effective Production of prodigiosin by native isolate *Serratia marcescence* MBB01. *Int Pharm Bio Sci.,* 4(1): (B):144-162.

Pradeep,B.V., Stanly Pradeep, F., Angayarkanni, J and Palaniswamy, M.2013. Optimization and production of prodigiosin from *Serratia marcescence* MBB05 using various natural substrates. *Asian Journal of Pharma and Clinical Research.*, Vol 6, Issue 1.

Priya, KA., Satheesh, S., Ashokkumar, B., Varalakshmi, P., Selvakumar, G and Sivakumar, N. 2013. Antifouling activity of prodigiosin from estuarine isolate of *Serratia marcescens* CMST07. In: Velu RK (ed) Microbiological research in agroecosystem management, vol XVI. Springer, New Delhi.

Priya, KA., Satheesh, S., Ashokkumar, B., Varalakshmi, P., Selvakumar G and Sivakumar, N. 2013. Antifouling activity of prodigiosin from estuarine isolate of Serratia marcescens CMST 07. In: Velu RK (ed) Microbiological research in agroecosystem management, vol XVI.Springer, New Delhi.

Priya, KA., Satheesh, S., Ashokkumar, B., Varalakshmi, P., Selvakumar, G and Sivakumar, N. 2013. Antifouling activity of prodigiosin from estuarine isolate of *Serratia marcescens* CMST07. In: Velu RK (ed) Microbiological research in agroecosystem management, vol XVI. Springer, New Delhi.

Pryce, L.H and Terry, F.W. 2000. Spectrophotometric assay of gene expression: *Serratia marcescens* pigmentation. *Bioscience.* 26: 3-13.

Pryce, LH and Terry, FW. 2000. Spectrophotometric assay of gene expression:*Serratia marcescens* Pigmentation. *Bioscene.*, 26(4):3-13.

Rahul K. Suryawanshi., Chandrashekhar D. Patil., Hemant P. Borase., Bipinchandra K. Salunke and Satish V.Patil. 2010. Studies on Production and Biological Potential of Prodigiosin by *Serratia marcescens*. *Appl Biochem Biotechnol.*, 173:1209–1221.

San-Lang, Wang., Chen-Yu, Wang., Yue-Horng, Yen., Tzu-Wen, Liang and Shin-Yi, Chen. 2012. Enhanced production of insecticidal prodigiosin from *Serratia marcescens* TKU011 in media containing squid pen. *Process Biochemistry.* 47:1684-1690.

Shahitha, S and Poornima, K. 2012. Enhanced Production of Prodigiosin Production in *Serratia Marcescens*. *J Applied Pharm Sci.*, 02 (08):138-140.

Shirata, A., Tsukamoto, P., Yasui, H., Hata, T., Hayasaka, S., Kojima, A and Kato, H. 2000. Isolation of bacteria producing bluish purple pigment and use for dyeing. *JARQ.*, 34: 131-140.

Silverman, M. P and Munoz, E. F .1973. Effect of iron and salt on prodigiosin synthesis in Serratia marcescens. *J. Bacteriol.*, 114: 999–1006.

Singh, B., Vishwakarma, RA and Bharate, SB. 2013. QSAR and pharmacophore modeling of natural and synthetic antimalarial prodiginines. *Curr Comput Aided Drug Des.*, 9:350–359.

Slater, H., Crow, M., Everson, L and Salmond, GP. 2003. Phosphate availability regulates biosynthesis of two antibiotics, prodigiosin and carbapenem in Serratia via quorum sensing- dependent and independent pathway, *Molecular microbiology*, 47: 303-32

Song Cang., Makoto Sanada.,Osamu Johdo., Shinji Ohta., Yasunori Nagamatsu and AkihiroYoshimoto. 2000. High production of prodigiosin by *Serratia marcescens* grown on ethanol. *Biotechnology Letters.*,22:1761–1765.

Soto-Cerrato, V., Llagostera, E., Montaner, B., Scheffer, G. L., and Pérez-Tomás, R.. 2004. Mitochondria-mediated apoptosis operating irrespective of multidrug resistance in breast cancer cells by the anticancer agent prodigiosin. *Biochem. Pharmacol.*, 68: 1345–1352.

Srijith, VM. 2006. Analysis of *Serratia marcescens* genome – identifying the biosynthetic pathway of the pigment prodigiosin –a computational approach.Williams, P., Bainton, NJ., Swift, S., Chhabra, SR., Winson, MK., Stewart, GSAB., Salmond, GPC and Bycroft ,BW. 1992. Small molecule mediated density dependent control of gene expression in prokaryotes:

bioluminescence and the biosynthesis of carbapenem antibiotics. *FEMS Microbiol. Lett.* 100: 161-168

Starr, MP., Grimont PAD, Grimont, F and Starr, PB. 1976. Caprylate thallous agar medium for selectively isolating *Serratia* and its utility in the clinical laboratory. *J Clin Microbiol.*, 4:270-276.

Staunton, J and Wilkinson, B. 1997. Biosynthesis of erythromycin and rapamycin. *Chem Rev.*, 97: 2611-2629.

Sumathi, C., MohanaPriya, D., Swarnalatha, S., Dinesh, M. G.,and Sekaran, G. 2014. Production of Prodigiosin Using Tannery Fleshing and Evaluating Its Pharmacological Effects. *The Scientific World Journal.*

Sundaramoorthy, N., Yogesh, P and Dhandapani, P.2009. Production of prodigiosin from *Serratia marcescens* isolated from soil. *Indian J Scie& Technoi.*, vol. 2(10).

Tzu-Wen Liang., Shin-Yi Chen., Yen-Chern Chen., Chia-Hung Chen., Yue-Horng Yen., and San-Lang Wang. 2013. Enhancement of Prodigiosin Production by *Serratia marcescens* TKU011 and Its Insecticidal Activity Relative to Food Colorants. *J Food Scie.,*vol 78(11).

Wang, SL., Peng, JH., Liang, TW and Liu, KC. 2008. Purification and characterization of a chitosanase from S. *marcescens* TKU011. *Carbohydr Res.*, 343:1316–23.

Wei, Y-H., Yu, W-J and Chen W-C .2005. Enhanced undecylprodigiosin production from Serratia marcescens SS-1 by medium formulation and amino-acid supplementation. *J Biosci Bioeng.*, 100:466–471.

Wei-Chuan Chen., Wan-Ju Yu., Chia-Che Chang., Jo-Shu Chang., Shih-Horng Huang., Chih-Hung Chang., Shan-Yu Chen., Chih-Ching Chien., Chao-Ling Yao., Wen-Ming Chen and Yu-Hong Wei. 2013. Enhancing production of prodigiosin from *Serratia marcescens* C3 by statistical experimental design and porous carrier addition strategy. *Biochem Eng.*, 78: 93-100.

Williams, RP and Hearn, WP. 1967 .Prodigiosin. In: Gottlieb, D., Shaw PD (eds) Antibiotics, vol. 2. Springer., New York, pp 410–432.

Witney, F. R., Failia, M. L., and Weinberg, E. D. 1977. Phosphate inhibition of secondary metabolism in Serratia marcescens. *Appl. Environ. Microbiol* ., 33: 1042–1046.

Yamashita, M., Nakagawa, Y., Li, H., and Matsuyama, T.2001.Silica gel-dependent production of prodigiosin and serrawettins by Serratia marcescensin a liquid culture. *Microb. Environ.*, 16: 250–254.

Yu-Hong Wei., Wan-Ju Yu and Wei-Chuan Chen.2005. Enhanced Undecylprodigiosin Production from *Serratia marcescens* SS-1 by Medium Formulation and Amino-Acid Supplementation. *Bioscience and Bioeng .*, 100(4): 466-471.

Printed in Great Britain
by Amazon

83423501R00037